BIRTHDAY BOOK of GEMS

We wish to thank the following museums for permitting us to photograph their treasures:

Smithsonian Institution, Washington D.C.;
Los Angeles County Museum of Natural History, Los Angeles, Ca.;
Deutsches Edelstein Museum, Idar-Oberstein, West Germany;
Museo el Oro, Bogota, Columbia.

Special thanks are due:

American Gem Society;
Gemological Institute of America;
American Gem Trade Association;
International Gem Trade Association.

The carvings on cover and pages 5 (hand), 35, 45, 57, and 81 are by Harold Van Pelt. Captions: Dr. Peter C. Keller and Alice S. Keller.

COVER PHOTOGRAPH The magnificient diamond jewelry is from the Harry Winston Collection. A 61.22-carat necklace with 215 diamonds flows from the egg. To the right is a 16.40-carat D-flawless pear shape diamond ring. A rare pair of fancy yellow diamond cuff links, totaling 42-carats, are next to a bracelet with 99 diamonds which weigh 45.75-carats. The faceted quartz hollow egg is mounted on a 363-carat fluted aquamarine pedistal with a quartz base and is 21 centimeters high.

First Edition 1986   Second printing 1987

Printed in Japan by Dai Nippon

Library of Congress Catalog Number. 86-090387

ISBN 0-9616485-0-3

BIRTHDAY
BOOK of
GEMS

PHOTOGRAPHS by
HAROLD and ERICA VAN PELT

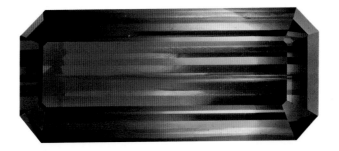

BIRTHSTONES

JANUARY	Garnet	JULY	Ruby
FEBRUARY	Amethyst	AUGUST	Peridot, Sardonyx
MARCH	Aquamarine, Bloodstone	SEPTEMBER	Sapphire
APRIL	Diamond	OCTOBER	Opal, Tourmaline
MAY	Emerald	NOVEMBER	Topaz, Citrine
JUNE	Pearl, Moonstone	DECEMBER	Turquoise, Zircon

WEEKDAY STONES

SUNDAY	Diamond
MONDAY	Pearl
TUESDAY	Ruby
WEDNESDAY	Amethyst
THURSDAY	Carnelian
FRIDAY	Emerald
SATURDAY	Turquoise

SEASONS STONES

SPRING	Emerald
SUMMER	Ruby
AUTUMN	Sapphire
WINTER	Diamond

ZODIAC STONES

AQUARIUS	1/21 — 2/21	Onyx, Malachite
PISCES	2/21 — 3/21	Jasper, Jade
ARIES	3/21 — 4/20	Carnelian
TAURUS	4/20 — 5/21	Topaz, Citrine
GEMINI	5/21 — 6/21	Emerald, Feldspar
CANCER	6/21 — 7/22	Ruby, Garnet
LEO	7/22 — 8/22	Sapphire, Lapis-Lazuli
VIRGO	8/22 — 9/22	Diamond, Beryl
LIBRA	9/22 — 10/23	Zircon, Turquoise
SCORPIO	10/23 — 11/21	Agate
SAGITTARIUS	11/21 — 12/21	Amethyst
CAPRICORN	12/21 — 1/21	Peridot, Chalcedony

PHOTOGRAPH OPPOSITE

This potpourri of jewelry, shown on a hand carved from rutilated quartz, represents some of the finest gemstones in the trade today. The pieces include a 35-carat blue sapphire ring, an 18-carat Thai ruby ring, a 32-carat padparadscha sapphire ring, a 29-carat canary yellow diamond ring, a canary yellow diamond bracelet, a ruby and diamond bracelet, and an emerald and diamond bracelet. Jewelry courtesy of Harry Winston, Inc.

FOREWORD

For hundreds of years, gemstones have been associated with specific dates, occasions, astrological signs, and other parts of the calendar. In recent years, certain gems have become well established as representing specific months, so that a person's birthstone is now an integral part of the birthday celebration.

Like the original birthday books of the 19th century, this gemstone Birthday Book indicates the dates for each month but not the specific day of the week. This makes it perfect for noting birthdays, anniversaries, and other special dates that repeat from year to year. For each month, the first photographs show both natural specimens and faceted or carved gems of the birthstone for that month. Other photographs show a wide variety of fine gems, jewelry pieces, and mineral specimens selected especially for this book from over a thousand pictures taken by Harold and Erica Van Pelt.

As an addition to the popular list of monthly gemstones, lists have also been included (on page 4) of birthstones for days of the week and astrological signs. This allows those who are not so taken with their birthstone on the standard list to make a selection from one of the other lists; giving an almost limitless choice, sure to please everyone who loves gemstones.

Not only is this Birthday Book a useful guide to all of us needing gentle reminders of important dates, but it is an esthetic delight and an educational asset as well.

Richard T. Liddicoat, Jr.
Chairman of the Board
Gemological Institute of America

MINERAL SUITE

OPPOSITE

Some of the most attractive minerals seen today are not gem materials and yet rival gems in their beauty and form. The lustrous black stibnite and bright red crocoite shown here are as exciting to behold as their gem cousin, a superb pink kunzite crystal.

JANUARY

1

2

3

4

5

6

TSAVORITE
GARNET

In 1972, a rich emerald-green variety of grossular garnet was found in the Taita Hills near the Tsavo Game Park in Kenya. The trade name Tsavorite was given the new gemstone by Campbell Bridges, the Scottish geologist who discovered the deposit. Tsavorite is one of the rarest varieties of garnet, the birthstone for January. Stones of good color that weigh more than a few carats are considered quite rare. This extraordinary 16.60-carat gem is one of the finest known examples of this new gemstone.

JANUARY

7

8

9

10

11

12

JADE
VASE

Jade has been held in high esteem by the Chinese for tens of centuries. It was not until the 18th century, however, that the most valuable form of jade, jadeite, was discovered in Burma. This extraordinary 35-centimeter-high vase from the Ch'ing Dynasty was carved from the rare and highly desirable lavender jadeite. It is part of the Smithsonian Institution collection.

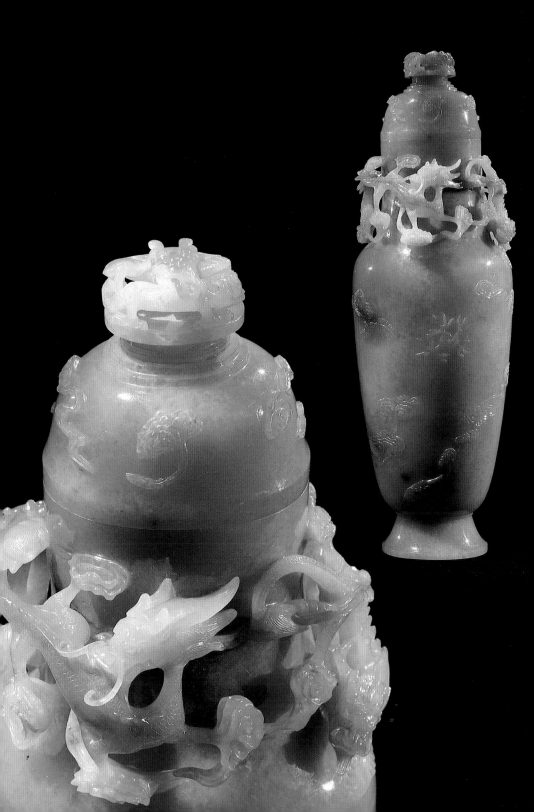

J A N U A R Y

13

14

15

16

17

18

DIAMOND
NECKLACE

This spectacular diamond necklace, from the famous gem collection of the Smithsonian Institution, contains 325 diamonds with a total weight of 131.43 carats. It
was donated to the Smithsonian by Lita Annenberg Hagen.

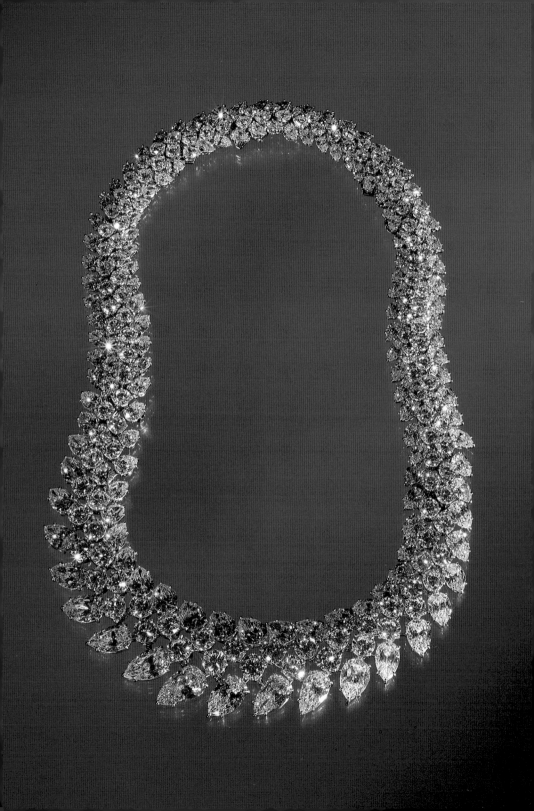

JANUARY

19

20

21

22

23

24

TOPAZ
CRYSTAL

Topaz is usually thought to be yellow. However, topaz also occurs in a multitude of other colors, of which blue is one of the most desirable. Because blue topaz most commonly is found as rounded stream cobbles, crystals of this gem material are highly prized by collectors. This 21-centimeter-high blue topaz crystal, with its coating of lepidolite, is from the Virgem da Lapa area of Minas Gerais, Brazil.

J A N U A R Y

25

26

27

28

29

30

31

TOURMALINES   One of the most fascinating attributes of tourmaline is the seemingly unlimited array of colors in which it occurs. This suite of 36 cut stones, ranging in weight from 3 carats to 56 carats, illustrates some of the more desirable colors. The rarest tourmalines are the bright blue stones that gemologists call indicolite.

FEBRUARY

1

2

3

4

5

6

AMETHYST

Amethyst, the birthstone for February, is one of the most historically important gemstones. For hundreds of years it has graced the fingers of popes as well as kings. Today, it is very popular in jewelry as faceted stones and beads, as well as in carvings. These beautiful carved amethysts were fashioned in Idar-Oberstein, West Germany, one of the world's greatest carving centers.

FEBRUARY

7

8

9

10

11

12

AMETHYST

Amethyst has been popular for centuries among European religious leaders and nobility alike. During the Middle Ages, an amethyst was believed to protect the wearer from getting overly intoxicated. In nature, amethyst most commonly is found in geodes. The most dramatic of these geodes are found in Rio Grande do Sul, Brazil, and adjoining areas in Uruguay.

FEBRUARY

13

14

15

16

17

18

TOURMALINE
NECKLACE

Tourmaline occurs in virtually every color. This majestic necklace represents an extraordinary collection of the many color varieties of tourmaline. The rarest occurrence is represented by the large multicolored stone in the center.

F E B R U A R Y

19

20

21

22

23

24

TOURMALINE
CRYSTAL

In 1978, an extraordinary pocket of red tourmaline, or rubellite, was uncovered at the Jonas mine in Minas Gerais, Brazil. This pocket contained literally tons of superb gem crystals, some of which were over a meter in length. This fine specimen exhibits the characteristic cranberry color associated with tourmalines from this famous discovery.

F E B R U A R Y

25

26

27

28

29

MOGUL
EMERALD

During the Spanish conquest of the area now known as Colombia, many fine emeralds were sent back to Europe. Several of the larger crystals were subsequently sold by the Spanish to Mogul nobility in India. This 217.8-carat emerald, known as the ''Mogul,'' exhibits beautiful craftsmanship. The floral motif on one side is typical of Mogul art; the Islamic prayer, written in Arabic, on the other side includes a date equivalent to 1695 A.D.

MARCH

1

2

3

4

5

6

AQUAMARINE   Aquamarine is the birthstone for March. Historically, significant amounts of fine gem aquamarine have been limited almost exclusively to the pegmatites of Minas Gerais, Brazil. Recently, however, the Nuristan region of Afghanistan has produced some fine aquamarine, as evidenced by this 75.8-carat faceted stone and almost 5-centimeter-high cluster of gem-quality crystals.

M A R C H

7

8

9

10

11

12

AQUAMARINE
CARVING

Aquamarine derived its name from the rich greenish blue color of seawater. These greenish blue aquamarine crystals are often quite large (gem-quality pieces weighing more than 35 kilos have been reported), and can therefore be carved. This fine 9-centimeter-high carving is from a workshop in Idar-Oberstein, West Germany.

M A R C H

13

14

15

16

17

18

HOPE
DIAMOND

Many important gemstones are known as much for the legends that surround them as for their intrinsic beauty. There is no better example of this than the infamous 45.52-carat Hope diamond. This rare, deep-blue diamond has been linked to the fall of French nobility, financial disaster in the Hope family for whom it is named, and untimely deaths in the families of its more recent owners. Today the Hope diamond is the centerpiece of the national gem collection in the Smithsonian Institution, to whom it was donated by world-famous jeweler Harry Winston.

MARCH

19

20

21

22

23

24

CARVED
ROCK CRYSTAL
VASE

This extraordinary 11.4-centimeter-high rock crystal vase is the work of a true craftsman. The vase exhibits 24 flutes on the body and the base. The natural quartz crystal from Arkansas in the background is typical of the material used to create fine pieces such as this. Although this vase was carved recently in the United States, the style is similar to work done by the great lapidaries of Ekaterinburg, Russia, in the late 19th century.

M A R C H

25

26

27

28

29

30

31

BERYL

The mineral beryl occurs in almost as many gem varieties as there are colors in the spectrum. The most important and valuable variety of beryl is emerald. However, blue-green aquamarine and golden yellow heliodor occur in much larger prismatic crystals, and can therefore be cut into stones of several hundred carats in weight, like those shown here.

APRIL

1

2

3

4

5

6

DIAMOND

Diamond, the birthstone for April, is undoubtedly the most popular of all gemstones. Because of the great hardness of diamonds and their unique brilliance and fire, gemologists have set them apart from all other gems. Diamonds usually occur in nature as eight-sided crystals known as octahedrons. To best use their natural form and unique optical properties, diamonds are most commonly fashioned into the 58-facet cut known as the standard round brilliant. This 5.08-carat round-brilliant-cut diamond is surrounded by a swirl of natural diamond crystals.

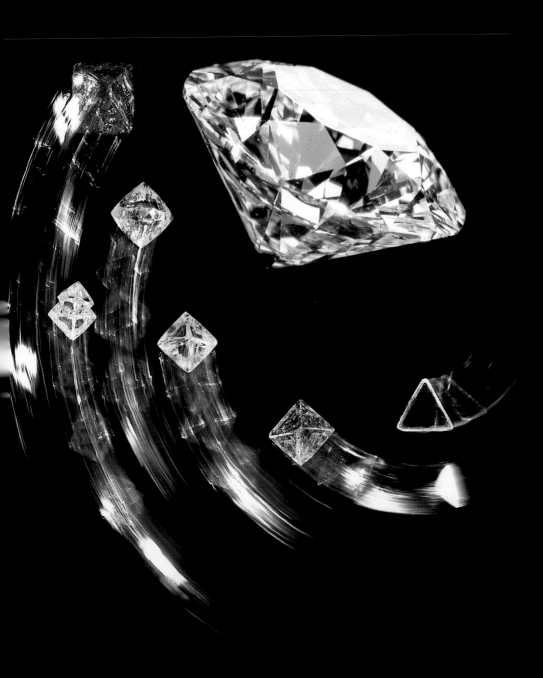

A P R I L

7

8

9

10

11

12

NAPOLEON
NECKLACE

Napoleon I presented this stunning diamond necklace to his wife, Empress Marie Louise, on the birth of their son in 1811. The necklace, which contains 47 diamonds totaling 275 carats, passed through many owners after the death of Empress Marie Louise in 1847. It was bequeathed to the Smithsonian Institution by heiress Marjorie Merriweather Post on her death in 1973.

APRIL

13

14

15

16

17

18

This diamond and opal dragon, by the famous 20th-century Italian designer Buccel-
lati, contains 750 diamonds which total almost 80 carats and an unusually fine fire
opal from Mexico. The opal, which displays the orange body color typical of
Mexican opals, is approximately 4 centimers high and 2.5 centimeters wide. The
entire dragon measures 12.5 centimeters in height.

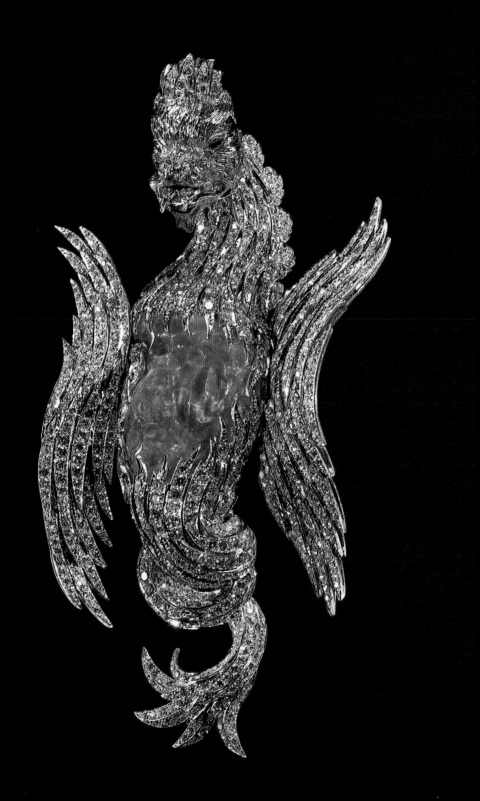

A P R I L

19

20

21

22

23

24

LAPIDARY
ART

The lapidary's art takes many forms, from faceting fine gemstones in both common and unusual shapes to carving intricate pieces like the rooster shown here. The unusual egg, a masterful mix of both carving and faceting, was fashioned from rock crystal with such precision that the two halves fit together perfectly at the gold rim. This faceted egg is shown with its base of aquamarine and rock crystal on the cover.

A P R I L

25

26

27

28

29

30

WULFENITE Some minerals possess all the beauty to compete with the rarest of gems, but are far too soft to be faceted or worn for adornment. This 4-centimeter-high wulfenite crystal from Sonora, Mexico, is one such example. Tabular wulfenite crystals are highly sought-after by sophisticated mineral collectors; the presence of an attractive associated mineral such as the orange mimetite seen here only enhances the value of the specimen.

M A Y

1

2

3

4

5

6

EMERALD   Through the ages, emerald, the birthstone for May, has been one of the most coveted of all gemstones. The infamous Roman emperor Nero found the color so soothing that he reputedly wore emerald glasses while watching the gladiators clash. Fine-colored emeralds without flaws are almost unknown. This 2.2-centimeter-high emerald crystal and its 1.66-carat faceted companion from Colombia are unique in both their superb blue-green color and their relative flawlessness.

M A Y

7

8

9

10

11

12

TOURMALINE   The Cruzeiro mine, in Minas Gerais, Brazil, has produced some of the finest green
tourmalines in the world. This unusual photograph shows twenty-five exposures of a
57-centimeter-high specimen of green tourmaline from Cruzeiro that is one of the
focal points of the mineral collection at the Los Angeles County Museum of Natural
History.

M A Y

13

14

15

16

17

18

GOLD

Through the ages, gold has been the most sought-after of precious meals. Although most gold occurs in particles no larger than a grain of sand, occasionally nuggets as large as several ounces and even pounds are found. The rarest forms of native gold occur as crystals, wires, or leaves; this 19-centimeter-high specimen of leaf gold from the Eureka mine in California is considered one of the finest examples in the collection of the Smithsonian Institution.

M A Y

19

20

21

22

23

24

GOLD
PECTORAL

This 19-centimeter-high gold pectoral from the Tolima area of Colombia was manufactured using the lost-wax method. The pre-Columbian Indians taught this technique to their Spanish conquerors, who subsequently introduced it into Europe. Unfortunately, many tons of beautiful pre-Columbian gold artifacts were melted down for bullion by the Spanish in their conquest of South America.

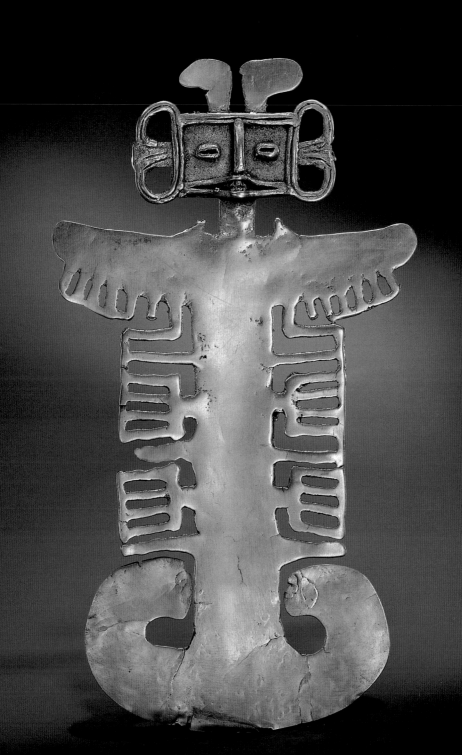

M A Y

25

26

27

28

29

30

31

ROCK CRYSTAL
VASES

This exceptional pair of rock crystal vases differ only in their caps of red and green gem tourmaline. Each vase is 26.6 centimeters high. Masterpieces such as these were usually created for the royal houses of Europe. Today, a few dedicated craftsmen continue the traditions of the Renaissance lapidaries.

J U N E

1

2

3

4

5

6

PEARLS

Many people think of pearls, the birthstone for June, as being perfectly round and found only in salt water. However, American Indians harvested baroque, or irregularly shaped, pearls from the fresh waters of the Mississippi River for hundreds of years. Today, baroque freshwater pearls are cultivated primarily in the Lake Biwa area of Japan. As this pendant attests, they can be quite beautiful. The 8-millimeter round pearls are fine-quality cultured saltwater pearls.

J U N E

7

8

9

10

11

12

TOURMALINE
SCEPTER

This 4.5-centimeter-high bicolored natural tourmaline scepter owes its unusual form to a turbulent growth history. The crystal may have originally been complete, but changing chemical conditions subsequent to growth could have caused the crystal to go back into solution.

J U N E

13

14

15

16

17

18

RUBELLITE
BEARS

Tourmaline is one of the most popular gem materials used for carving in the 20th century. Early in this century, literally tons of California tourmaline was shipped to China, where it was fashioned by local artisans into objects for the Chinese nobility. These exquisite pink tourmaline bears represent the high degree of craftsmanship and imagination found in Idar-Oberstein, West Germany, today.

J U N E

19

20

21

22

23

24

Fine jadeite is coveted the world over, but particularly by the Chinese. The most sought-after variety of jadeite, and that which was historically reserved for nobility, is the rich green imperial jadeite. This particularly fine 25-carat carving is from the Hixon Collection of the Los Angeles County Museum of Natural History.

J U N E

25

26

27

28

29

30

BICOLORED
TOURMALINE

Not only does tourmaline occur in an endless array of colors, but a single crystal of tourmaline may exhibit more than one color. A crystal with two colors is known as a "bicolor"; if more than two colors are present, the crystal is called "particolored." The fine bicolored crystals and faceted stones shown here are from the famous Himalaya mine, San Diego County, California.

J U L Y

1

2

3

4

5

6

The most coveted of all colored gemstones is undoubtedly the birthstone for July, ruby. This extraordinary 10.02-carat ruby ring and the accompanying 14.54-carat (total weight) ruby earrings, all surrounded by diamonds, are truly befitting of royalty.

J U L Y

7

8

9

10

11

12

RUBY
EAGLE

Ruby is second only to diamond in hardness and therefore is very difficult to carve. Usually, only the most experienced lapidaries will attempt to work with this difficult precious gem. This exceptional ruby eagle, which weighs 809 grams and has a 36.3-centimeter wingspan, is the work of lapidaries from Idar-Oberstein, West Germany.

J U L Y

13

14

15

16

17

18

MARIE
ANTOINETTE
EARRINGS

Marie Antoinette, the wife of Louis XVI of France, was noted for her extravagant tastes and especially for her extraordinary diamond jewelry. We get an idea of just how lavish her collection was with these diamond earrings, which weigh a total of over 35 carats. These earrings were reputedly taken from her just before she met her death at the guillotine in 1793. They are now part of the gem collection of the Smithsonian Institution.

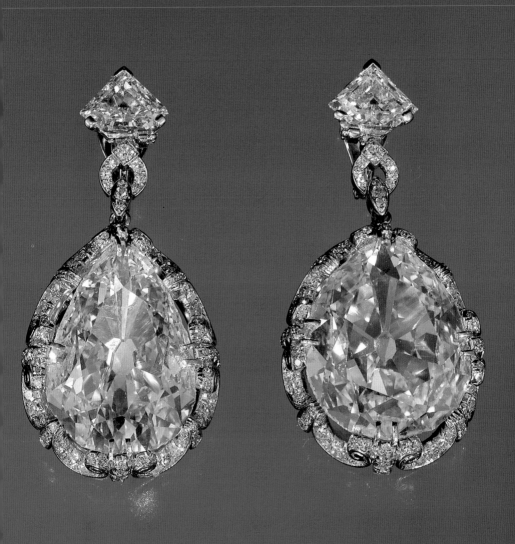

J U L Y

19

20

21

22

23

24

BENITOITE
CRYSTAL

The relatively new gemstone benitoite is found only in the Diablo Mountains of San Benito County, California. Since it was discovered in 1906, only small amounts of this material have been mined. Today, benitoite remains one of the rarest gemstones in the world, and California has claimed it as its official state gemstone. This 1-centimeter crystal on matrix is shown here using three different photographic angles.

J U L Y

25

26

27

28

29

30

31

BENITOITE
NECKLACE

When benitoite was first discovered, it was thought to be sapphire because of the similarities in color and other gemological properties. Later it was determined to be an entirely new mineral species. The most spectacular example of this rare gemstone in jewelry is this necklace, which contains 52 faceted benitoites, the largest of which is 4.2 carats. An unusually rare and fine crystal of benitoite is shown in the preceding photo.

AUGUST

1

2

3

4

5

6

PERIDOT

The birthstone for August is the rich yellow-green gem, peridot. Although peridot historically has been found on St. John's Island in the Red Sea, or in upper Burma, today most peridot on the world's market has been mined by Apache Indians on their reservation at San Carlos, Arizona. The peridots shown here, which include a 20-carat ring and a 30-carat pendant, are probably from the mines in upper Burma.

AUGUST

7

8

9

10

11

12

AGATE
CARVINGS

The Idar-Oberstein region of West Germany has been a center for stone carvings for more than a thousand years, an industry stimulated by the once-vast deposits of agate found in the surrounding area. Over the centuries, beautiful bowls and other containers have been carved from the local material. Today, although the local deposits have been depleted, the carving industry still thrives, using agate and other materials imported from around the world.

A U G U S T

13

14

15

16

17

18

AGATE

Unusually patterned agate can be an object of natural art and beauty. This closeup photograph of a thinly sliced section of agate from Brazil attests to just how magnificent a simple piece of this material can be.

AUGUST

19

20

21

22

23

24

RHODOCHROSITE The rich red color of fine rhodochrosite makes this a popular mineral with sophisticated collectors. This 9-centimeter-high specimen of rhodochrosite with a beautiful spray of quartz was found in the lead-silver mines of Peru. It is now one of the most prized specimens in the mineral collection of the Smithsonian Institution.

AUGUST

25

26

27

28

29

30

31

LAPIS-LAZULI
PEACOCK

Although most people think of gems only in terms of faceted stones, the art of carving gem materials has been practiced for literally thousands of years. This exquisite peacock is carved out of lapis-lazuli from Afghanistan and studded with rubies.

SEPTEMBER

1

2

3

4

5

6

SAPPHIRES   Although sapphire, the birthstone for September, is most commonly thought to be blue, it actually occurs in almost any color. The most desirable colors for sapphire are the rich, velvety Kashmir blue and the pinkish orange padparadscha. These sapphires are from the Hixon Collection of the Los Angeles County Museum of Natural History.

SEPTEMBER

7

8

9

10

11

12

BLUE
SAPPHIRE

Often rarer than a well-cut gem is a well-formed natural crystal of the same material. This beautiful pair of blue sapphire crystals, the largest of which is 3.5 centimeters high, are particularly well formed and gemmy. Fine crystals such as these are occasionally found in the gem gravels of Sri Lanka.

SEPTEMBER

13

14

15

16

17

18

NATIVE
SILVER

Silver in its pure form can occur as crystals or wires. Specimens from the centuries-old mines of Kongsberg, Norway, often take on unusual shapes that can be considered natural works of art. This 15-centimeter-high wire of Kongsberg silver, from the mineral collection of the Los Angeles County Museum of Natural History, is one such specimen.

SEPTEMBER

19

20

21

22

23

24

BLUE SAPPHIRE
NECKLACE

A fine blue sapphire is one of the most highly prized members of the gem kingdom. Today Sri Lanka, a small island located off the southeastern tip of India, produces most of the world's finest blue sapphires. This 17.22-carat blue sapphire, mounted in a classic baroque-inspired necklace, is a superb example of a fine sapphire from Sri Lanka. It is accented with twelve brilliant-cut diamonds totaling 2.37 carats.

SEPTEMBER

25

26

27

28

29

30

BERYL

Although the rich green emerald is the best known, beryl occurs in a great number of varieties based on color. These include the greenish blue aquamarine, salmon pink morganite, golden yellow heliodor, and colorless goshenite, as well as red beryl and pale green beryl. All of these varieties are commonly found in nature as long six-sided prisms.

OCTOBER

1

2

3

4

5

6

OPAL
PENDANT

Opal, the birthstone of October, owes its great beauty to the unique property known as play-of-color, whereby opal can exhibit flashes of many spectral colors at the same time. As the stone is turned, these flashes of color may change. The most desirable color flashes are red. This 17-carat black opal from Lightning Ridge, New South Wales, Australia, displays particularly fine play-of-color. This necklace was created by Cartier in 1937.

OCTOBER

7

8

9

10

11

12

LION
PIN

The art of jewelry making can be as effective as any other art form. This contemporary lion pin is at once fanciful and powerful. It has been designed and executed with as much intensity and style as a fine painting, and yet adds the excitement of natural gold, platinum, and pavéd diamonds.

OCTOBER

13

14

15

16

17

18

AQUAMARINE   Fine crystals of gem-quality aquamarine are rare. They historically have come from Brazil. This 6.25-centimeter-high crystal, with a collar of white albite feldspar, is particularly rare because it was found in the Fano Simmons mine, a gem-bearing pegmatite in Riverside County California.

OCTOBER

19

20

21

22

23

24

"RAM'S HORN"
GOLD

This 5-centimeter wire of native gold is aptly called the "Ram's Horn." Because of its unusual form, it is one of the rarest specimens of gold on public display today. This specimen, now in the collection of the Los Angeles County Museum of Natural History, was found near Leadville, Colorado, in 1878. It reputedly was owned by Dr. David H. Dougan, mayor of that famous gold-mining center.

OCTOBER

25

26

27

28

29

30

31

CUSTODIA DE
SAN IGNACIO

In the 16th and 17th centuries, wealthy landowners in the Spanish colony now known as Colombia paid their respects to the Roman Catholic Church by commissioning incredible altar pieces fashioned from gold and studded with emeralds and other precious stones. Few of the church treasures remain today, since most were melted down in the 19th century to help pay for the wars of liberation. Today, one of the most extraordinary church treasures remaining in Colombia is this *custodia*, which consists of approximately 8.5 kilograms of gold and over 1,480 emeralds.

NOVEMBER

1

2

3

4

5

6

IMPERIAL
TOPAZ

The most desirable variety of topaz, the birthstone for November, is found only in an area around the colonial city of Ouro Preto in Minas Gerais, Brazil. Because of its rich reddish orange hue, this variety is referred to as ''imperial'' topaz in the gem trade. This 6-cm-high crystal and the two faceted stones (19.21 and 17.78 carats, respectively) exhibit the stunning color for which imperial topaz is known.

N O V E M B E R

7

8

9

10

11

12

BLUE
TOPAZ

Although topaz is commonly thought to be only yellow, it actually occurs in many colors. Recently, blue topaz has become very popular, particularly as a natural substitute for aquamarine. This 17-centimeter-high crystal and 182-carat faceted blue topaz are superb examples of how beautiful blue topaz can be.

NOVEMBER

13

14

15

16

17

18

CAMEO
BOWL

One of the finest examples of the lapidary's art is that of the cameo carving. Some of the most spectacular cameo carvings ever made are those done in the form of agate bowls, like this intricately carved 20-centimeter-diameter bowl from Idar-Oberstein, West Germany. It may take an experienced craftsman such as Richard Hahn, who carved this bowl, over a year to complete such a piece.

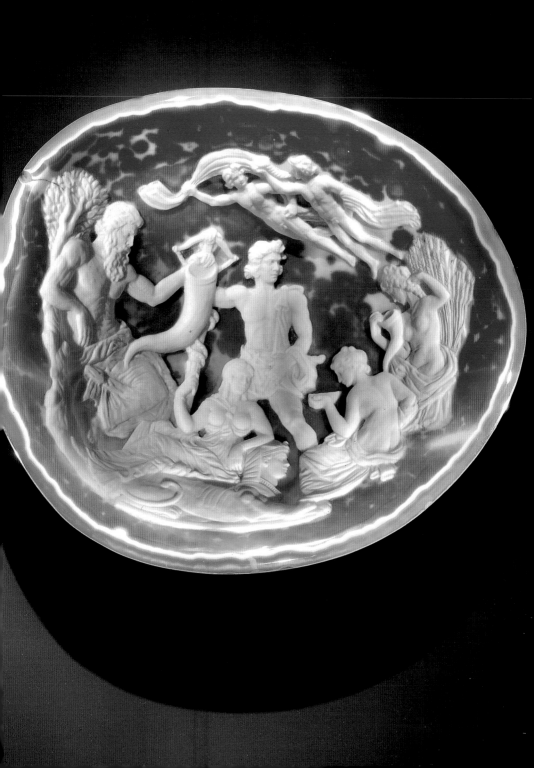

NOVEMBER

19

20

21

22

23

24

SAPPHIRE
AND
CHRYSOBERYL

Minute inclusions in a gemstone, if properly oriented, may interact with reflected light to give the gem a special appearance. If the inclusions are oriented in one direction, chatoyancy—or a cat's-eye effect—is created. If the inclusions are oriented in three directions, asterism—or a star effect—is seen. This 11.44-carat cat's-eye chrysoberyl and 36.18-carat blue star sapphire are superb examples of what gemologists call "phenomenal" stones.

NOVEMBER

25

26

27

28

29

30

AQUAMARINE
AND
CITRINE

Using an innovative faceting technique, Bernd Munsteiner of Idar-Oberstein, West Germany, has created rare and unusual gems from flawless material. This 145-carat aquamarine and 206-carat citrine are superb examples of his sense of dimension and proportion.

DECEMBER

1

2

3

4

5

6

MARIE LOUISE
DIADEM

Reputedly, this diadem was given to Empress Marie Louise, wife of Napoleon I, on the birth of their son in 1811. The crown consists of over 950 diamonds, which total approximately 700 carats, and 79 turquoise cabochons, which total 540 carats. The crown originally contained emeralds, but these were sold and replaced by turquoise early in the 20th century. The diadem was bequeathed to the Smithsonian Institution by heiress Marjorie Merriweather Post. Turquoise is the birthstone for December.

DECEMBER

7

8

9

10

11

12

ZIRCON

Zircon is the alternate birthstone for the month of December. The colorless and blue varieties are most popular, although zircon may also occur in green, brown, orange, or red. Because of its high degree of dispersion, or fire, it has traditionally been used as a diamond simulant. The 23.85-carat blue zircon and 23.07-carat colorless zircon shown here are from the Hixon Collection of the Los Angeles County Museum of Natural History.

DECEMBER

13

14

15

16

17

18

RUTILE
IN
QUARTZ

Virtually all gemstones, as they develop, can trap other minerals. Generally, these inclusions detract from the beauty of the gem. In some instances, however, the inclusions may actually enhance the stone. Such is the case with these beautiful starbursts of rutile that have been entrapped in quartz from Brazil.

DECEMBER

19

20

21

22

23

24

KUNZITE

The relatively rare, yet very beautiful, gemstone kunzite was first found in 1906 near Pala, in San Diego County, California. Today, the Pala area produces very little kunzite; most comes from Brazil or Afghanistan. This 56.19-carat heart-shaped stone and 8-centimeter-high crystal, however, are from one of the original Pala discoveries.

DECEMBER

25

26

27

28

29

30

31

PENDANT   This late-19th-century pendant from the Gleim Collection contains a spectacular array of fine colored gemstones. The 17-75-carat golden sapphire is surrounded by demantoid garnets, and the 10.25-millimeter pearl is flanked by two red spinels. A rare 2.67-carat demantoid garnet forms the bottom of the pendant. The entire piece is accented by diamonds.

Erica and Harold Van Pelt photographs have appeared in most major publications dealing with gems and minerals.

Publications include: *Gem and Crystal Treasures, Gemstones* and *Noble Metals,* Time-Life Books; *The Gem Collection of the Smithsonian,* the Smithsonian Institution; *Brazil-Paradise of Gemstones; Emerald and Other Beryls;* and *Gemstones of North America.*

Periodicals regularly featuring their photographs are: *Gems & Gemology; The Mineralogical Record; Lapidary Journal; Modern Jeweler; Pacific Jeweler* and *Jewelers Circular Keystone.*

During their long career, they have traveled extensively, photographing gems and minerals for museums and private collectors.